SCOOBY-DOO!
SPOOKTASTIC
JOKE BOOK

Published by the Penguin Group
Penguin Books Ltd, 80 Strand, London WC2R 0RL, England
Penguin Group (USA) Inc., 375 Hudson Street, New York, New York 10014, USA
Penguin Group (Canada), 90 Eglinton Avenue East, Suite 700, Toronto, Ontario, Canada M4P 2Y3
(a division of Pearson Penguin Canada Inc.)
Penguin Ireland, 25 St Stephen's Green, Dublin 2, Ireland (a division of Penguin Books Ltd)
Penguin Group (Australia), 250 Camberwell Road, Camberwell, Victoria 3124, Australia
(a division of Pearson Australia Group Pty Ltd)
Penguin Books India Pvt Ltd, 11 Community Centre, Panchsheel Park, New Delhi – 110 017, India
Penguin Group (NZ), 67 Apollo Drive, Mairangi Bay, Auckland 1310, New Zealand
(a division of Pearson New Zealand Ltd)
Penguin Books (South Africa) (Pty) Ltd, 24 Sturdee Avenue, Rosebank, Johannesburg 2196, South Africa

Penguin Books Ltd, Registered Offices: 80 Strand, London WC2R 0RL, England

penguin.com

Published 2006
1

Made and printed in England by Clays Ltd, St Ives plc

British Library Cataloguing in Publication Data
A CIP catalogue record for this book is available from the British Library

ISBN-13: 978–0–141–31930–8
ISBN-10: 0–141–31930–5

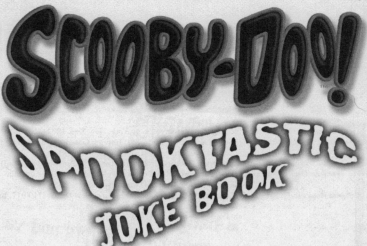

SCOOBY-DOO!
SPOOKTASTIC JOKE BOOK

Richard Dungworth

PUFFIN

CLASSIC CREEPS

VAMPIRE
KEY CREEPY CHARACTERISTICS
- freaky fangs
- batty behaviour
- likes hanging around in crypts and vaults
- thirst for blood

TOP MYSTERY INC. TIPS
If he asks you round for a bite,
say 'No fangs' . . .

Don't ask him how
he likes his stake . . .

WEREWOLF

KEY CREEPY CHARACTERISTICS
- serious body-hair problem
- tendency to wolf down the unsuspecting
- moons around at night, howling a lot

TOP MYSTERY INC. TIPS
Be suspicious of anyone who combs their face . . .

WHAT DRINKS BLOOD AND QUACKS?
Count Duckula.

WHY DOESN'T ANYONE LIKE THE VAMPIRE OF SKULL ISLAND?
He's a pain in the neck.

What is Dr Coffin's favourite ice-cream flavour? VEINILLA.

SHAGGY:
HEY, SCOOBY — LIKE,
WHAT'S THE TALLEST TOWER
IN TRANSYLVANIA?
SCOOBY:
RI RON'T ROH, RAGGY.
SHAGGY:
THE VAMPIRE STATE
BUILDING, OLD BUDDY!

WHAT CAN YOU DO IF YOU'RE
CRAZY ABOUT DRACULA?
Join his fang club.

HOW DO VAMPIRES LIKE
THEIR CAPPUCCINO?
Decoffinated.

THE VAMPIRE

Worried that your best friend *might* be a vampire? Answer these quick questions to find out whether he's the real fang, or just a little batty . . .

1. HOW OLD IS YOUR FRIEND?
a) 6–9 years
b) 10–12 years
c) 200+ years

2. HOW DOES HE TEND TO DRESS?
a) trainers and casual clothes
b) the very latest fashionable gear
c) black cloak, black patent shoes, bow tie

3. WHAT IS HIS MOST STRIKING FEATURE?
a) his general good looks
b) his physique
c) his fangs

4. IF YOU CUT YOURSELF IN HIS PRESENCE, DOES HE:

a) get you a plaster?

b) go a bit woozy at the sight of your blood?

c) drool uncontrollably?

5. WHERE DOES HE LIKE TO HANG OUT?

a) at your house

b) at the park

c) in the local graveyard

6. WHAT TV PROGRAMME DOES HE PARTICULARLY DISLIKE?

a) anything with Anne Robinson
b) boring documentaries
c) *Buffy*

7. WHEN YOU HAVE A SLEEPOVER AT HIS HOUSE, DOES HE OFFER YOU:

a) a sleeping bag?
b) the bottom bunk?
c) his spare coffin?

8. IF YOU PLAY CRICKET, WHICH DOES HE PREFER TO BE:

a) bowler?
b) fielder?
c) bat?

9. WHEN HE HAS A CARTON OF JUICE, DOES HE:

a) drink it with a straw?
b) empty it into a glass?
c) bite two holes in it and suck it dry?

10. WHERE DOES HE TEND TO GO ON HOLIDAY?

a) somewhere in Britain
b) somewhere warmer
c) Transylvania

IF YOU ANSWERED MOSTLY C, THERE'S A FAIR CHANCE YOUR MATE IS A BATTY BLOODSUCKER. WE ADVISE THAT YOU EAT PLENTY OF GARLIC, ONLY AGREE TO MEET HIM IN DAYLIGHT, AND WEAR A HIGH-NECKED SWEATER AT ALL TIMES.

What goes 'Von, three, tvelve – I vant to drink your blood'?
CAN'T COUNT DRACULA.

WHY ARE SMALL VAMPIRES THE ONES TO FEAR MOST?
Because they're a little batty.

WHERE DOES THE VAMPIRE OF SKULL ISLAND GO ON HOLIDAY?
The Isle of Fright.

WHERE DO WEREWOLF MOVIE STARS LIVE?
HOWL-LYWOOD.

WHERE DO CHINESE VAMPIRES COME FROM?
Fanghai.

GHOST/GHOUL/PHANTOM/SPECTRE

KEY CREEPY CHARACTERISTICS
- Floats about in deserted mansion/ castle etc.
- often see-through
- moans a lot
- not very touchy-feely

TOP MYSTERY INC. TIPS
Get on a ghost's good side by using polite Spirit World etiquette:

APPROPRIATE GREETINGS
- 'How do you boo?'
- 'Nice to see through you.'
- 'How's death?'

APPROPRIATE FAREWELLS
- 'Take scare of yourself.'
- 'Creep in touch.'
- 'Spook to you later.'

WHICH AIRLINE DOES THE TECHNICOLOUR PHANTOM ALWAYS FLY WITH?

British Scareways.

WHY DID THE HEADLESS SPECTRE GO INTO BUSINESS?

He wanted to get ahead in life.

THEN THERE WERE THE TWO GHOSTS WHO FELL IN LOVE THE INSTANT THEY MET. IT WAS LOVE AT FIRST FRIGHT.

FRED'S TOP READS

When **WEREWOLVES** Attack
by Claudia Armov

101 Great Plans BY MAJOR D. ZASTER AND GENERAL MAYHEM

MYSTERY VEHICLE MISHAPS BY M.T. TANKE

HYPNOTIZING SPOOKS BY N. TRANCE

CLASSIC MONSTERS BY FRANK N. STINE

What type of streets are most often haunted?
DEAD ENDS.

WHERE DOES REDBEARD'S GHOST GO ON HOLIDAY?
MALI-BOO.

Why do the Diabolical Disc Demon and the Gator Ghoul hang out together?
BECAUSE DEMONS ARE A GHOUL'S BEST FRIEND.

WHAT DO GHOSTS EAT FOR DINNER?
SPOOKHETTI OR
GHOULASH.

Why did the Ghostly Gondolier
buy stilts for his kids?
TO RAISE THEIR SPIRITS.

SHAGGY: DO YOU KNOW
WHAT YOU CALL A
GHOST'S MUM AND DAD,
SCOOB?
SCOOBY: RUH-HUH.
SHAGGY: LIKE, HIS
TRANS-PARENTS, MAN!

THE UNDEAD CHARTS
CURRENT TOP FIVE SINGLES

1 **JUMP (OUT OF YOUR SKIN)** — Ghouls Aloud

2 **HEXEL F.** — Crazy Hag

3 **STAYIN' UNDEAD** — The Heebee-Geebies

4 **BETTER THE DEVIL YOU KNOW** — Zombie Minogue

5 **BANDAGE RAP** — Puff Mummy

HIGHEST NEW ENTRY

9 **FREAK LIKE ME** — Shivababes

WHY ARE GHOSTS BAD AT TELLING LIES?

BECAUSE YOU CAN SEE RIGHT THROUGH THEM.

What kind of music do ghosts like best?
SOUL, OR RHYTHM AND BOOS.

WHO WAS THE MOST FAMOUS GHOST DETECTIVE?
Sherlock Moans.

Where does Geronimo's ghost live?
IN A CREEPY TEPEE.

CREEPY CORPSES

ZOMBIE

KEY CREEPY CHARACTERISTICS
- animated corpse
- rotten company
- favours a nice swamp or misty marshland

TOP MYSTERY INC. TIPS
Never tell a zombie to 'Get a life' . . .

MUMMY

KEY CREEPY CHARACTERISTICS
- bandage-wrapped
- enjoys a good moan
- found in ancient Egyptian tombs
- dead smelly

TOP MYSTERY INC. TIPS
Avoid teasing – they don't like
being wound up . . .

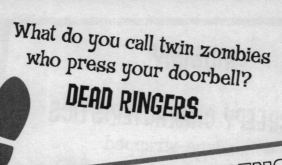

What do you call twin zombies
who press your doorbell?
DEAD RINGERS.

WHAT'S THE DIFFERENCE
BETWEEN A SONGWRITER
AND A ZOMBIE?
One composes, the other decomposes.

WHO DID THE MOMBA ZOMBIE
INVITE TO HIS PARTY?
Anyone he could dig up.

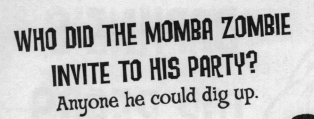

Why don't
mummies make
good listeners?
THEY'RE TOO
WRAPPED UP IN
THEMSELVES.

WHAT DOES THE NO-FACE ZOMBIE
HAVE FOR BREAKFAST?
RICE CREEPIES.

DAPHNE'S TOP READS

SPOTTING BOOBYTRAPS
by Luke Owte

The 10,000 Volt Ghost: A Study
BY ALEC TRICITY

Keep Your Looks
BY FAY SLIFT

BLUNDERS TO AVOID
BY MISS TAKES AND MISS HAPS

The Giant Book of Monsters
BY HUGH MUNGOUS

WHY DON'T MUMMIES GO ON HOLIDAY?
In case they relax and unwind.

ARE ZOMBIES GOOD IN A CRISIS?
NO - THEY GO TO PIECES.

Why were ancient Egyptian children often confused?
BECAUSE THEIR DADDIES WERE MUMMIES.

Funny Bones

Here are some rattling good skeleton gags to tickle your funny bone!

Rones? Rum-rum!

WHY CAN'T SKELETON MEN PLAY ROUSING CHURCH HYMNS?

They have no organs.

WHO WAS THE MOST FAMOUS FRENCH SKELETON?

Napoleon Bone-apart.

Who is in charge
of a class of
young skeletons?
A SKULL
TEACHER.

WHAT DO SKELETON
MEN ORDER AT A
RESTAURANT?
SPARE RIBS.

What do you call a skeleton who won't
get up in the morning?
LAZY BONES.

WHY DIDN'T THE SKELETON MAN
GO TO THE BALL?
He had no body to dance with.

HANDY HIEROGLYPHICS

It is important to get along with your mummy. Communication is the key. Try using these handy hieroglyphic messages to make that important connection.

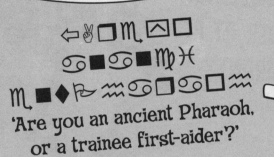

'Are you an ancient Pharaoh, or a trainee first-aider?'

'What scent are you wearing? It's *so* distinctive.'

'I've heard all about Tutankhamun – are you his mummy?'

'May I sign your bandages?'

'*Lovely* tomb. And no need for a window cleaner. Very practical.'

'Goodness me – that must have been *some* accident!'

Witches and Warlocks

WITCH

KEY CREEPY CHARACTERISTICS
- warty old hag
- pointy black hat
- gifted speller
- likes a good cackle

TOP MYSTERY INC. TIPS
Don't criticize her broomstick handling – she might fly off the handle . . .

WARLOCK

KEY CREEPY CHARACTERISTICS
- wizard at magic tricks
- brews up trouble with poisonous potions
- hex-tremely dangerous

TOP MYSTERY INC. TIPS
A long white beard and
pointy hat spells trouble . . .

WHY DO WITCHES WEAR NAME TAGS?
So, they know which witch is which.

WHO WAS THE MOST FAMOUS WIZARD DETECTIVE?
WARLOCK HOLMES.

WHY WON'T MERLIN WEAR
A FLAT HAT?
HE CAN'T SEE THE POINT.

WHAT DO YOU CALL A ONE-LEGGED WITCH?
EILEEN.

VELMA'S TOP READS

EXPERT INVESTIGATING
by Seymour Cloos

SOLVING MYSTERIES
BY N. IGMA

RECOGNIZING ROBOTS
by Anne Droyde

The Mathematics of
Mystery-solving
BY ADAM UPP

WHY CHOOSE GLASSES?
BY LEN SIZHURT

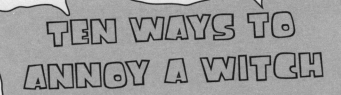

TEN WAYS TO ANNOY A WITCH

1. Swap the 'Eye Of Toad' and 'Sherbert Lemons' labels on the jars in her pantry.

2. Coat her wand in superglue.

3. Tell her she's looking lovely today.

4. Dye her cat's fur white.

5. Buy her an 'I ♥ Hansel & Gretel' cauldron cover.

6. Fix L-plates on her broomstick.

7. Borrow her cauldron to make popcorn.

8. Tell her you're not sure black is her colour.

9. Stick a big letter D on her pointy hat.

10. Correct her spelling.

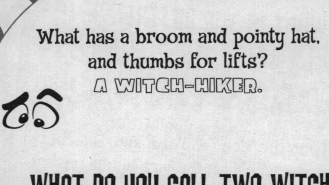

What has a broom and pointy hat,
and thumbs for lifts?
A WITCH-HIKER.

WHAT DO YOU CALL TWO WITCHES WHO SHARE AN APARTMENT?

Broom-mates.

WHAT IS THE DIFFERENCE
BETWEEN WARLOCK ANTHOS
AND THE LETTERS
M, A, K, E AND S?

One makes spells, the
other spells 'makes'.

What goes cackle, cackle, bonk?
A WITCH LAUGHING HER
HEAD OFF.

WHAT DO YOU CALL A WITCH WHO
DRIVES REALLY BADLY?

A road hag.

HOW MANY MEMBERS OF MYSTERY INC. DOES IT TAKE TO CHANGE A LIGHT BULB?

Five – Fred to come up with a plan, Scooby to disguise himself as an electrician and change the bulb, Daphne to discover the switch triggers a secret trapdoor, Velma to crawl around in the darkness looking for her glasses, and Shaggy to make the multi-decker submarine sandwiches.

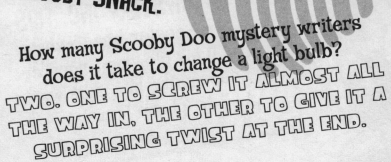

How many Great Danes does it take to change a light bulb?

ONE. BUT ONLY FOR A SCOOBY SNACK.

How many Scooby Doo mystery writers does it take to change a light bulb?

TWO. ONE TO SCREW IT ALMOST ALL THE WAY IN, THE OTHER TO GIVE IT A SURPRISING TWIST AT THE END.

ALIENS AND ANDROIDS

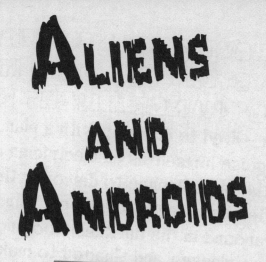

ALIEN

KEY CREEPY CHARACTERISTICS
- odd-coloured (often green)
- drives a saucer-shaped vehicle
- calls you 'Earthling'
- hasn't heard of David Beckham

TOP MYSTERY INC. TIPS
Don't pester him to show you his glowing finger, or keep asking him if he wants to 'phone home'...

ANDROID

KEY CREEPY CHARACTERISTICS

- made of metal
- batteries included
- droning, teacher-like voice
- doesn't like swimming

TOP MYSTERY INC. TIPS

See how his
supercomputer brain
copes with having
his shoelaces
tied together . . .

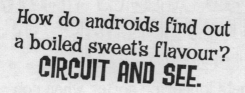

How do androids find out
a boiled sweet's flavour?
CIRCUIT AND SEE.

WHAT DO YOU CALL AN
ALIEN SPOOK WITH TWELVE
EYES, FIVE EARS, TWO
MOUTHS, FOUR ARMS AND
ONE LEG?
Anything you like – he'll never
catch you.

What do
alien spooks call Shaggy
and Scoob?
UNIDENTIFIED
FLEEING
OBJECTS.

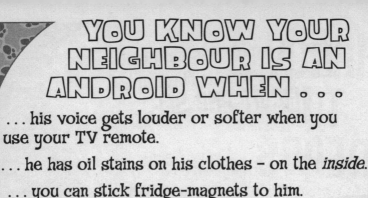

YOU KNOW YOUR NEIGHBOUR IS AN ANDROID WHEN . . .

. . . his voice gets louder or softer when you use your TV remote.

. . . he has oil stains on his clothes – on the *inside*.

. . . you can stick fridge-magnets to him.

. . . he has rust behind his ears.

. . . he gives off a very quiet humming noise.

. . . you catch him with a finger in your battery recharger.

. . . his Things To Do list says 'oil change', but he doesn't own a car.

. . . he's seen the film *Robots* more than three hundred times.

. . . if he gets caught in the rain, he gives off blue sparks and talks gibberish.

. . . he falls in love with your washing machine.

SHAGGY'S TOP READS

THE COWARD'S SURVIVAL GUIDE
by Hugo First

MOUTH-WATERING MULTI-DECKERS
BY SAM WIDGE

Looking After Number One
BY XAVIER SELPH

SURVIVING LOCH NESS
BY RHODA BOTE

THE ULTIMATE CHILLI COOKBOOK
BY IVOR WINDYBOTTOM

DOCTOR JEKYLL'S DOCTOR JOKES

SHAGGY: Doctor, I'm having *real* creepy nightmares about monsters under my bed. Like, what can I do?

DOCTOR: Saw the legs off your bed.

DOCTOR: Is the anti-werewolf medicine I gave you working, sir?

PATIENT: Oh, yes, absolutely. I'm completely fine nooooOOOOOOWWW!

DAPHNE: Doctor, I keep having a strange dream about a giant praying mantis on a carousel.

DOCTOR: Don't worry - it's just a bug that's going round.

MONSTROUS BEASTS

MONSTER/BEAST

KEY CREEPY CHARACTERISTICS

- anything from a terrifying pterodactyl to a deeply creepy sea monster
- weird-looking
- usually hungry
- unsuitable for inviting to a sleepover

TOP MYSTERY INC. TIPS

The Loch Ness Monster, the Demon Shark, the Beast of Bottomless Lake, the Kelp Monster – you can deal with them all with the same master stroke. Front crawl!

WHAT DO YOU DO WITH A GREEN MONSTER?

Wait until it ripens.

WHICH MONSTER IS THE BIGGEST PRACTICAL JOKER?

Prankenstein.

WHAT ARE BLACK AND STICKY AND SMELL BAD?

The Tar Monster's socks.

What's the Snow Beast's favourite cereal? ICE CRISPIES.

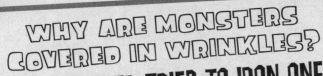

WHY ARE MONSTERS COVERED IN WRINKLES? HAVE YOU EVER TRIED TO IRON ONE?

WHERE DO OWL MEN STRUT THEIR STUFF?
At a talon contest.

What kind of music does the Stone Creature like best? **ROCK.**

SCOOBY'S TOP READS

SCARY SKELETON OR TASTY SNACK?
by Nora Boan

AVOIDING THE MUG'S JOBS
by Y. Mee

The Canine Holiday Guide
BY KEN NULLS

RELAXATION FOR DOGS
by Leah Bowt

EMERGENCY SCOOBY-SNACKING
BY JUSTIN CASE

What does a prehistoric caveman preserved in ice have for breakfast?
DE-FROSTIES.

WHICH MONSTER IS THE BEST DANCER?
THE BOOGIEMAN.

What happens if you come face to face with the Beast of Bottomless Lake?
YOU'RE IN DEEP TROUBLE.

SPOOKY LIMERICKS

Ve've saved ze verse till last . . .

A **werewolf** with quite frightful bite,
Used to howl at the moon every night.
It wasn't because
He was carnivorous
But just that his pants were too tight.

A **vampire** who liked his blood hot,
Would warm up a pint in a pot.
Once convinced it was done,
He would down it in one
(As it otherwise tended to clot).

A **witch** who lived over the ocean,
Once cooked up a terrible potion.
    Just one drop of this brew
    Turned you fluorescent blue,
Which tended to cause a commotion.

A huge, hairy, fearsome-toothed **Yeti**
Made the local folk nervous and sweaty.
    But their worries were eased
    When it turned out the beast
Lived solely on tins of spaghetti.

A **zombie** whose looks
    provoked dread,
Had grown fed up of acting
    undead.
    All the groaning and gore
    Had become such a bore
That he'd taken up knitting
    instead.

There once was an **alien** creature,
Who posed as an infant school teacher.
She'd be nice as could be,
As you learned ABC,
Then she'd sneak up behind you and eatcha.

A **vampire** with blood-curdling fangs,
Used to suffer unusual pangs.
He had no lust for blood
(As a true vampire should)
But instead craved ice cream and meringues.

A **phantom** who haunted a castle
Found scaring off people a hassle
For they'd not flee in fright
But just laugh at the sight
Of his hat, which was pink, with a tassel.